RHYMES FOR ANNIE ROSE

D1465065

For Elsa Madeleine

RHYMES
FOR ANNIE ROSE
SHIRLEY HUGHES

Red Fox

A Picture of Annie Rose

Two brown eyes,
One pink nose,
Ten busy fingers,
Ten pink toes.
Colour in her brown curls,
Colour in her clothes,
Colour in a big smile
And that's Annie Rose.

Chirpy

All the house is quiet,
Curtains tightly drawn,
But someone sings a little song
To welcome in the dawn.

It's not time for breakfast,
Too soon to play,
But someone's very chirpy
And ready for the day.

Heads deep in pillows,
Underneath the clothes,
But all the birds are wide awake
And so is Annie Rose.

Old Friends

There's little Teddy One Ear and Teddy Big,
Daffodil, my knitted duck, and Portly Pig,
Mr Bones and Bonny and Raggedy Ann
And dear old Buttercup, my white woolly lamb.

Elizabeth has eyes that open and close,
Hair that you can brush and comb and very pretty clothes.
There's a white dress for a wedding and a pink one for a ball –
But I still love Buttercup best of all.

Patiently waiting, ready to play,
From when I wake up till the end of the day,
And close beside me the whole night through,
They're only toys but they're old friends too.
It would never do to tell the rest
That I love Buttercup the best.

Duck Weather

Splishing, splashing in the rain,
Up the street and back again,
Stomping, stamping through the flood,
We don't mind a bit of mud.
Running pavements, gutters flowing,
All the cars with wipers going,
We don't care about the weather,
Tramping hand in hand together.
We don't mind a damp wet day,
Sloshing puddles all the way,
Splishing, splashing in the rain,
Up the street and back again.

Teatime

Lickery, stickery, jammery jee,
Buttery toast and buns for tea.
Bears like honey and so do we,
So eat your crusts up, one, two, three.
A bite for you and a bite for me,
Lickery, stickery, jammery jee!

Bernard

I like Bernard.
Rough Bernard,
Tough Bernard,
Stop-it-that's-quite-enough Bernard,
Playing pirates, running races,
Wrinkled socks and trailing laces,
Funny jokes and wild faces,
Falling-about Bernard,
Scuffle-and-shout Bernard,
I like Bernard.

Footprints

We went out, and in the night
All the world had turned to white.
Snowy garden, snowy hedge,
Ice along the window ledge.
And all around the garden seat
A tiny bird with tiny feet
Had left his footprints in the snow,
As he went hopping to and fro.

Teeny Tiny

A stocking full of presents,
Open each with care,
A toy watch and a shiny ball,
A chocolate teddy bear,
And something at the bottom
That I never knew was there –
A teeny tiny dolly
With bright yellow hair.

She wears a teeny tiny dress,
A teeny tiny wrap,
And teeny tiny shoes to match
Her teeny tiny cap.
I'll keep her in my pocket,
Look after her with care,
My teeny tiny dolly
With the bright yellow hair.

Mouse?

Tick, tock, dickory dock,
Where is the mouse
Who ran down the clock?
I've looked in the cupboard,

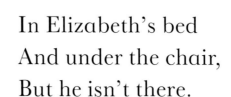

In Elizabeth's bed
And under the chair,
But he isn't there.

I've looked on the stair,

No hint of a whisker,
No wriggly pink nose,
Where has he gone to?
Nobody knows.
Tick, tock, dickory dock,
Oh, where is the mouse
Who ran down the clock?

Night Flight

Annie flew out of the window,
Bedclothes and cot and all,
And floated around above the ground,
And over the garden wall.

And her shadow skimmed over the gardens
And followed her all the way,
As she looked down on the roofs of the town
And the moon shone as bright as day.

Fingers

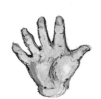

One little finger
Dancing on her own,
Joined by another one,
Now she's not alone.
Up jumps the middle one,
Strong and tall,

Here comes the fourth one,
Liveliest of all.
Stubby old Tom Thumb
Has nowhere to go,
Put him with the others
And there's five in a row.

Toes

Beatie Bo,
Big toe.
Mrs Moore,
Next door.
Solomon Riddle,
In the middle.
Lucky Jim,
Next to him.
And last of all,
Curled up small,
Fat little Billy Ball.

Houses

Come around to my house,
Knock at the door,
And we'll have a tea party
Sitting on the floor.

I'll come to your house,
Bring a friend as well,
Tap at the window,
Ring at the bell.

You can stay at my house,
Just for a treat.
I'll give you lots of fizzy drinks
And lovely things to eat.

I could come to your house,
Visit you instead.
I could stay forever –
Or till it's time for bed.

The Knobbly Tree

The knobbly tree
Is wider than me
With a secret place
Where it's safe to be.
A hollow you can creep inside,
A sort of room where you can hide.
And no one can see
Alfie and me
When we're snug as two bugs
In the knobbly tree.

Bedtime *(with salutations to A.A.Milne)*

What is the matter with Annie Rose?
Nothing would please her today.
She wouldn't have stories or sit on my lap,
She was far too bad-tempered to play.
Lunchtime was awful, quite a disgrace –
Carrots and gravy all over the place!
And when did you ever see such a cross face?
She wasn't her best today.

But now that it's nearly time for bed
She's having a change of mood.
She built me a castle and sang me a song
And chatted and laughed and cooed.
She ate up her supper and asked for some more,
No bits of banana or crust on the floor,
She's the best behaved person that I ever saw –
What can have made her so good?

Shipwreck

Little wooden sailor,
Brand new boat.
Take them to the pond
And set them afloat.

Makes a large tidal wave
Shaped like a V,
Very choppy weather
Far out at sea.

Wind begins to carry them
Far from the beach,
Jauntily sailing
Way out of reach.
Fine white daddy duck
Decides to take a swim,
Waddles to the water,
Lunges in.

Catches little sailor
Quite by surprise –
Boat and captain
Both capsize!
Nearly under water,
Bobbing up and down.
Will the boat go under?
Will the sailor drown?

Dog to the rescue
Right up to her neck,
Strikes out bravely
Straight for the wreck.

Head above water,
Paddling with her paws,
Takes the wooden sailor
Safely in her jaws.
Someone finds a long stick,
Hauls the boat in.

Dog lands sailor,
Gives a big grin.
Shaggy coat, sopping wet,
Long dripping ears,
Looks about, pleased as punch,
Everybody cheers.
Boat and sailor
Both safe and sound.
Dog gives her coat a shake
And soaks us all around!

Girl Friends

Marian, Lily and Annie Rose
Are three bonny girls, as everyone knows.
Sometimes bouncy, sometimes sad,
Sometimes sleepy, sometimes glad,
Sometimes grubby, sometimes clean,
Often kind, though sometimes mean.
But most of the time they try to be good,
And to all that know them it's understood
That Marian, Lily and Annie Rose
Are best of friends, as everyone knows.

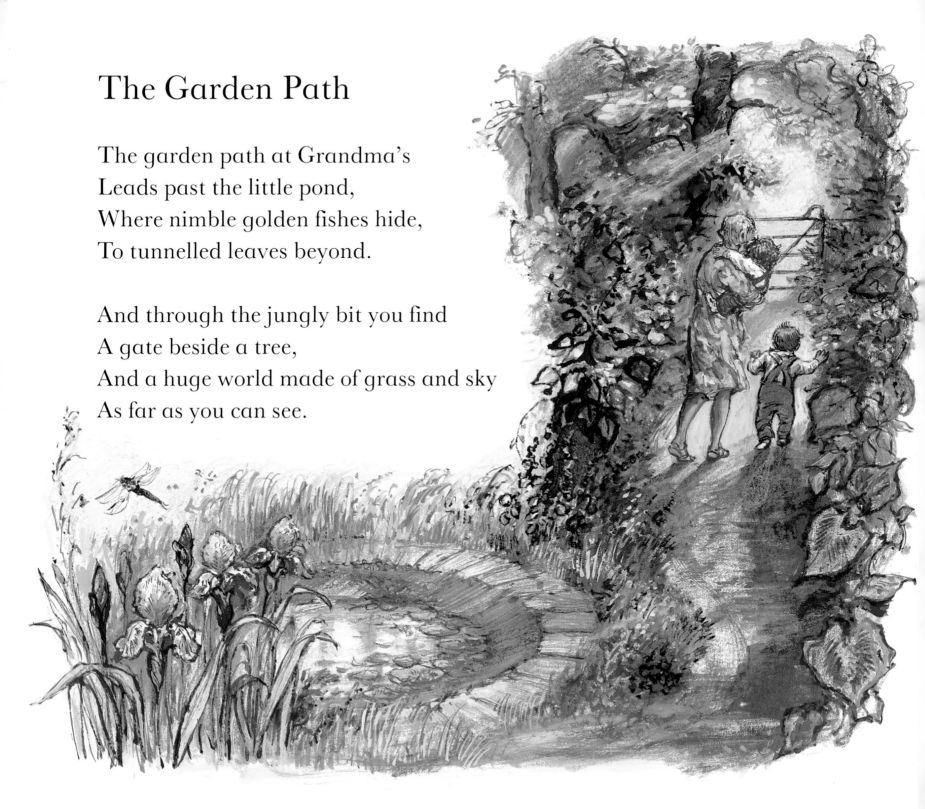

The Garden Path

The garden path at Grandma's
Leads past the little pond,
Where nimble golden fishes hide,
To tunnelled leaves beyond.

And through the jungly bit you find
A gate beside a tree,
And a huge world made of grass and sky
As far as you can see.

Summer Numbers

Ten tall aerials, pointing at the sky,
Nine brown birds, swooping by,
Eight parked cars, baking in the street,
Seven pretty flower pots, lined up neat,
Six hot schoolboys, trailing home late,
Five friendly neighbours, chatting by the gate,
Four lazy cats, sitting in the shade,
Three laughing ladies, sipping lemonade,
Two squealing children, playing with the hose,
One of them is Alfie and the other's –
Annie Rose!

A Red Fox Book
Published by Random House Children's Books
20 Vauxhall Bridge Road, London SW1V 2SA
A division of Random House UK Ltd
London Melbourne Sydney Auckland
Johannesburg and agencies throughout the world
Copyright © Shirley Hughes 1995
1 3 5 7 9 10 8 6 4 2
First published in Great Britain by
The Bodley Head Children's Books 1995
Red Fox edition 1997
All rights reserved
Printed in Hong Kong
RANDOM HOUSE UK Limited Reg. No. 954009
ISBN 0 09 946491 8